THIS BOOK BELONGS TO

- -

- -

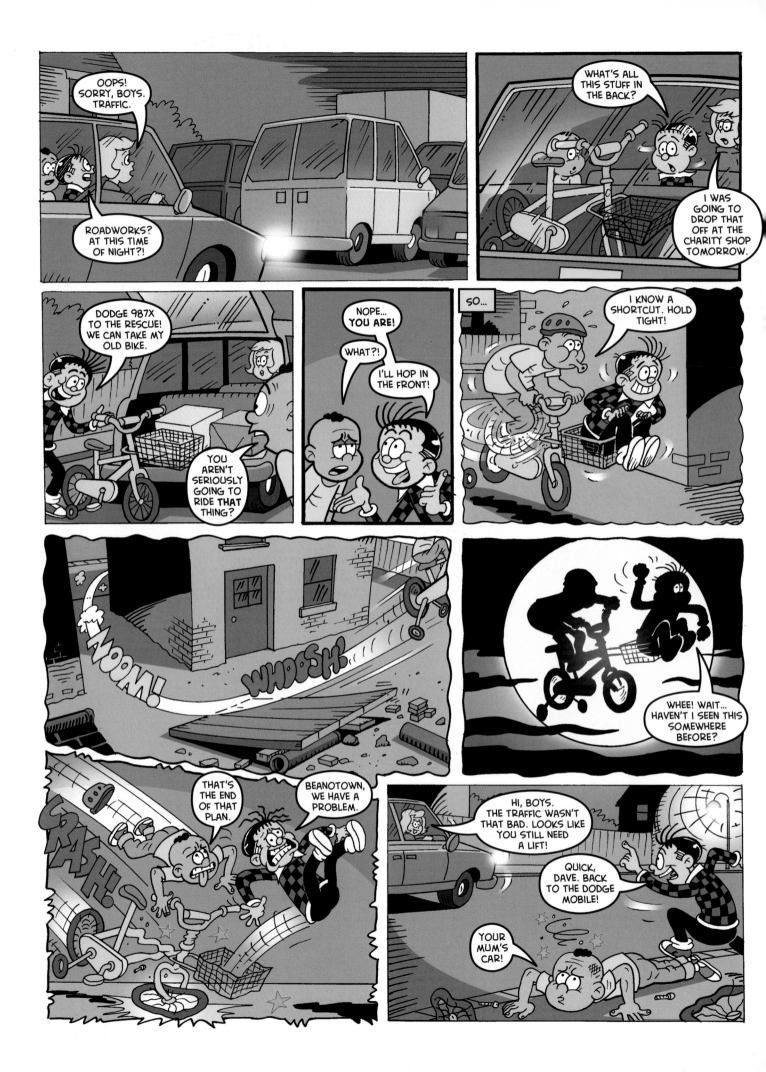

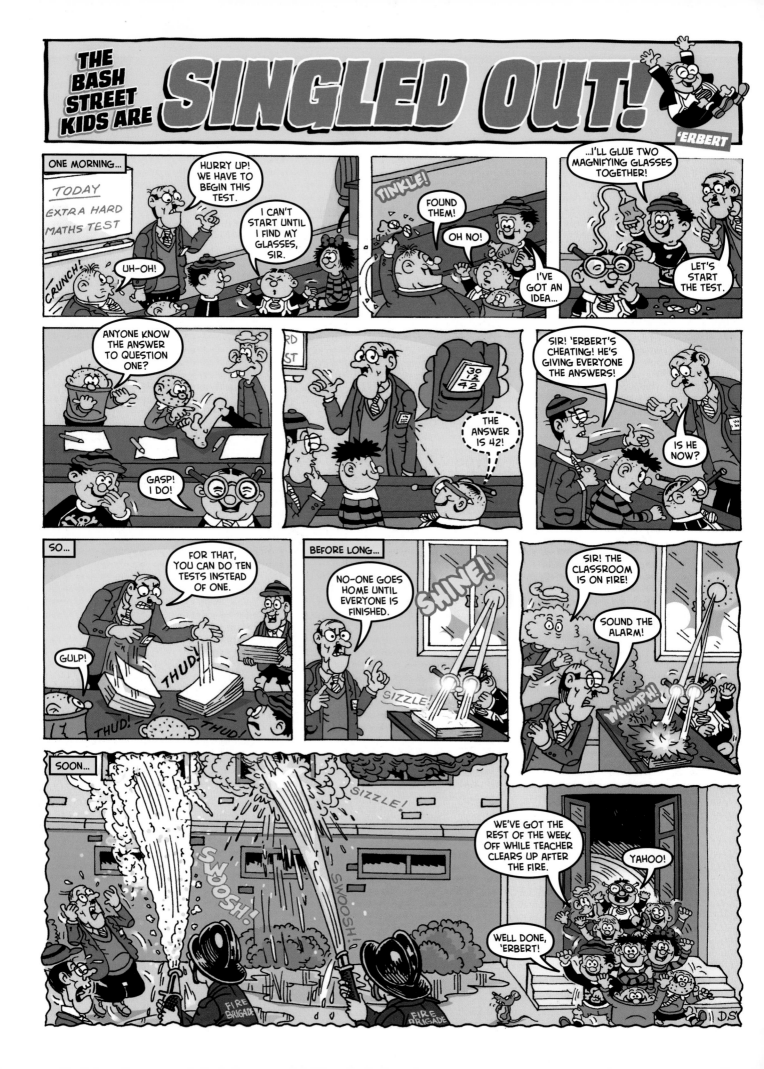

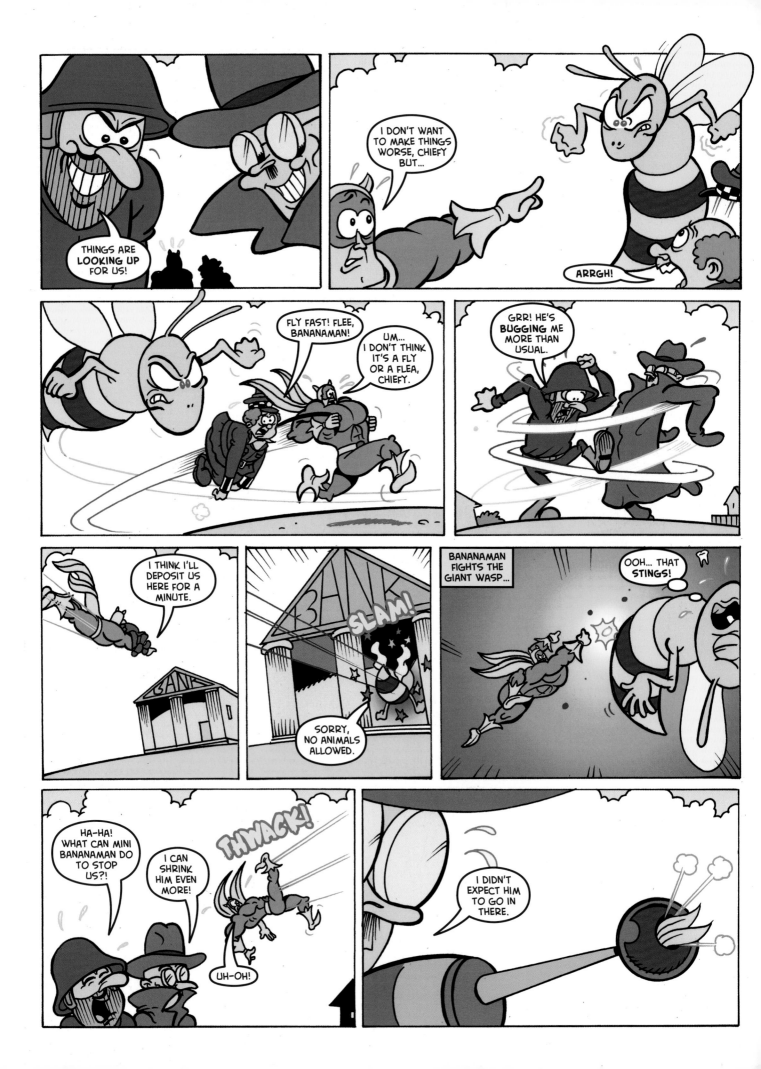

SHRINK YOU CAN SOLVE IT?

General Blight and Doctor Gloom have used their shrink-o-ray to shrink some things in Beanotown and to make other things bigger. Can you find the five things they've shrunk and the six things they made bigger?

NUMSKULLS

The Little guys that Live in your head! Everybody has them!

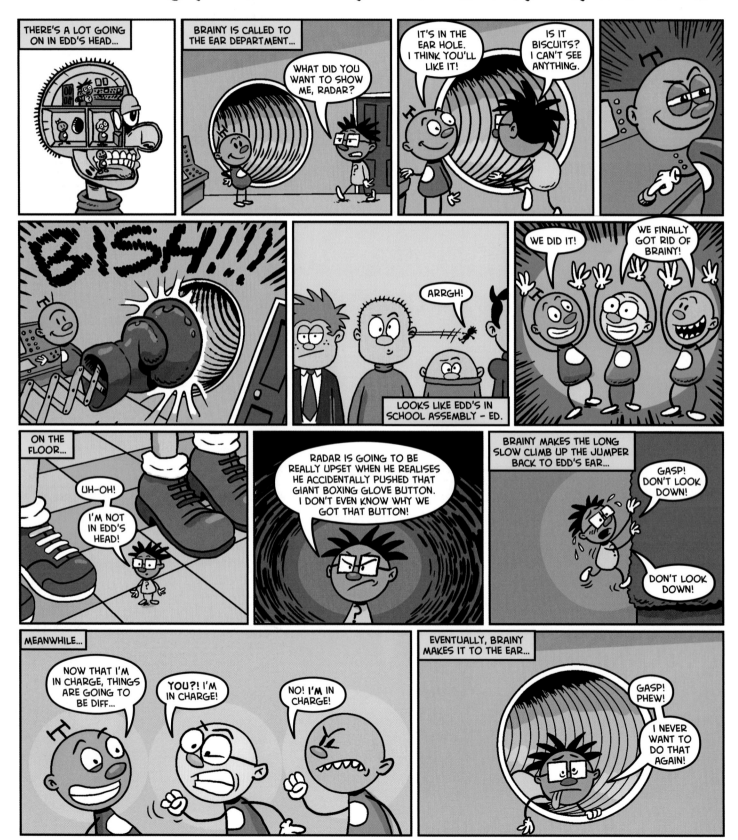

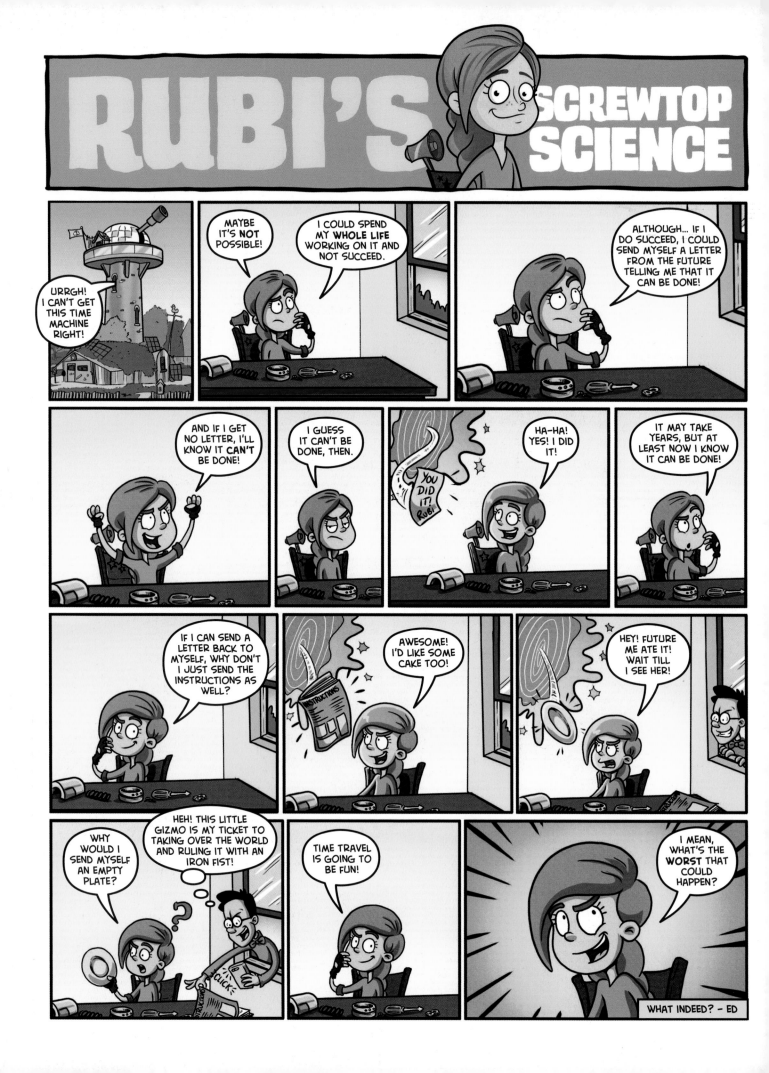

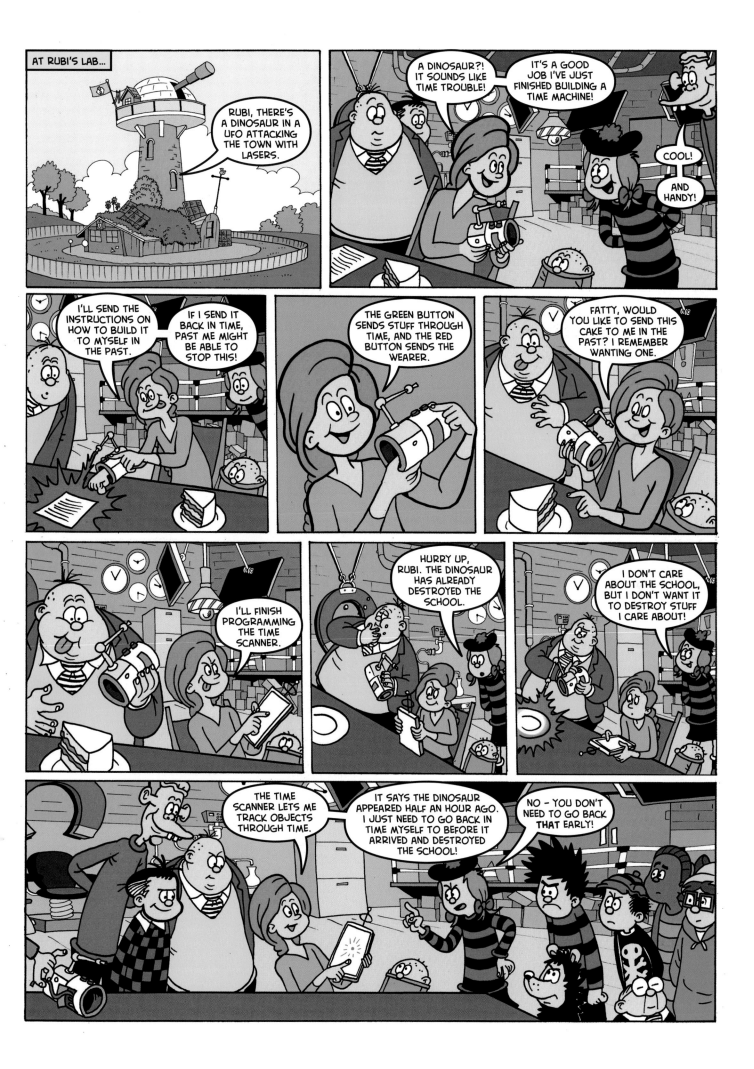

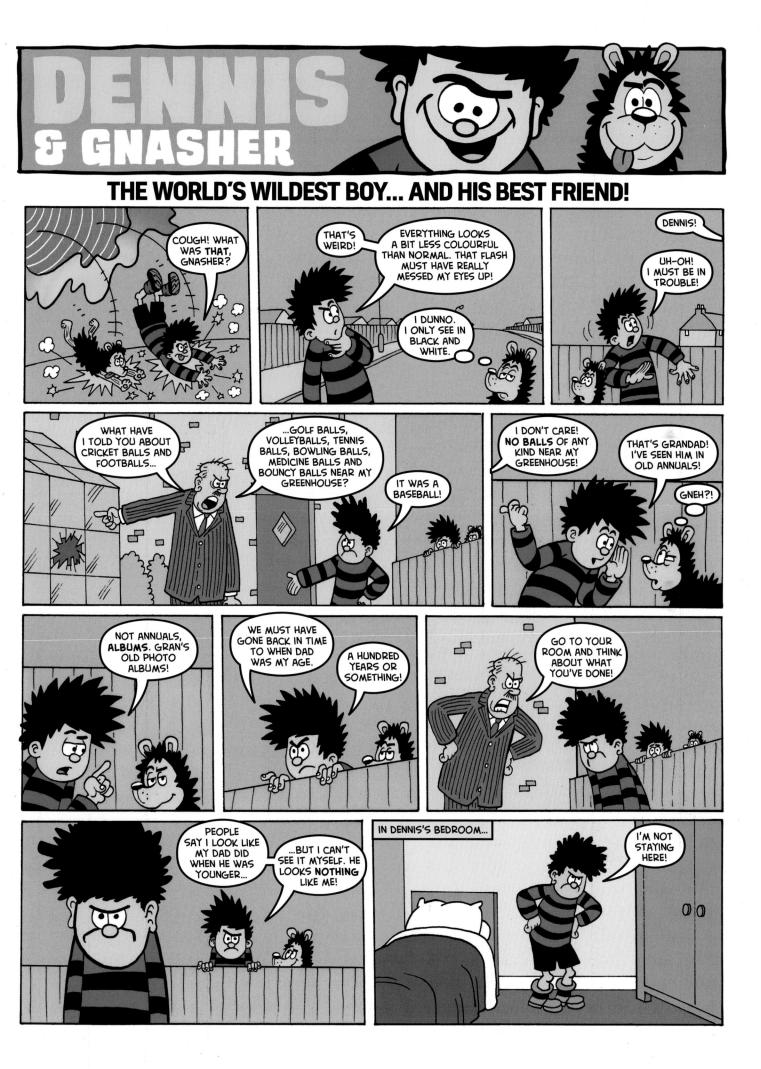

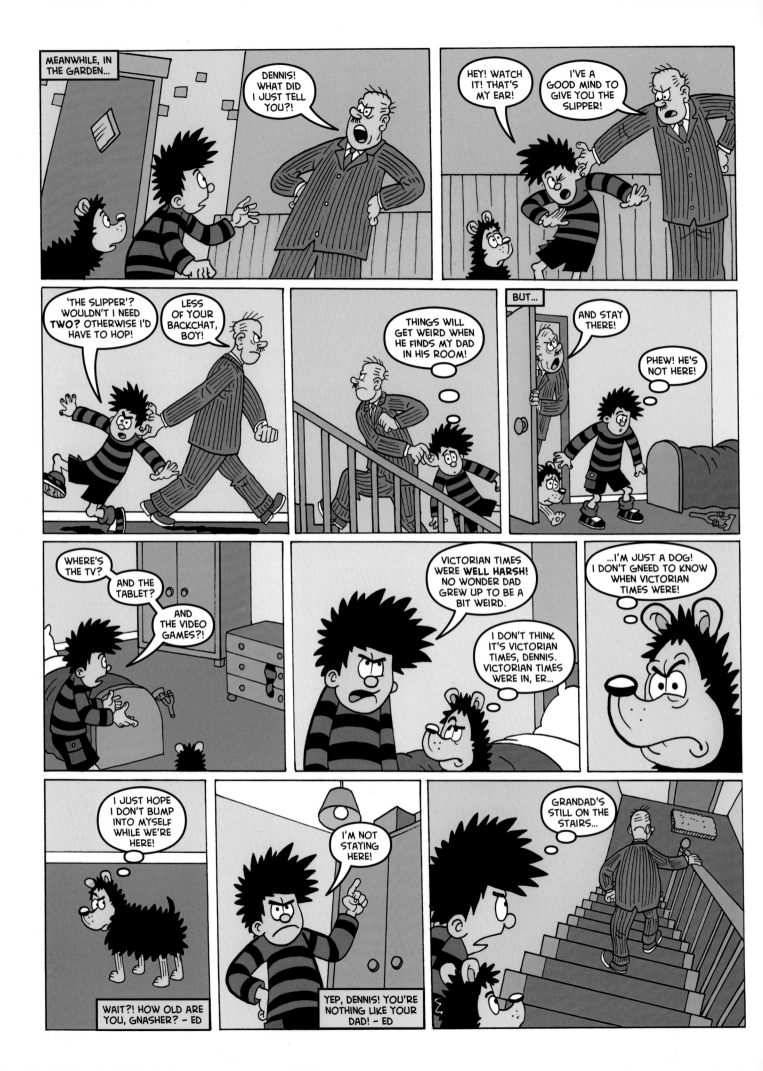

NUMSKULLS

The Little guys that Live in your head! Everybody has them!

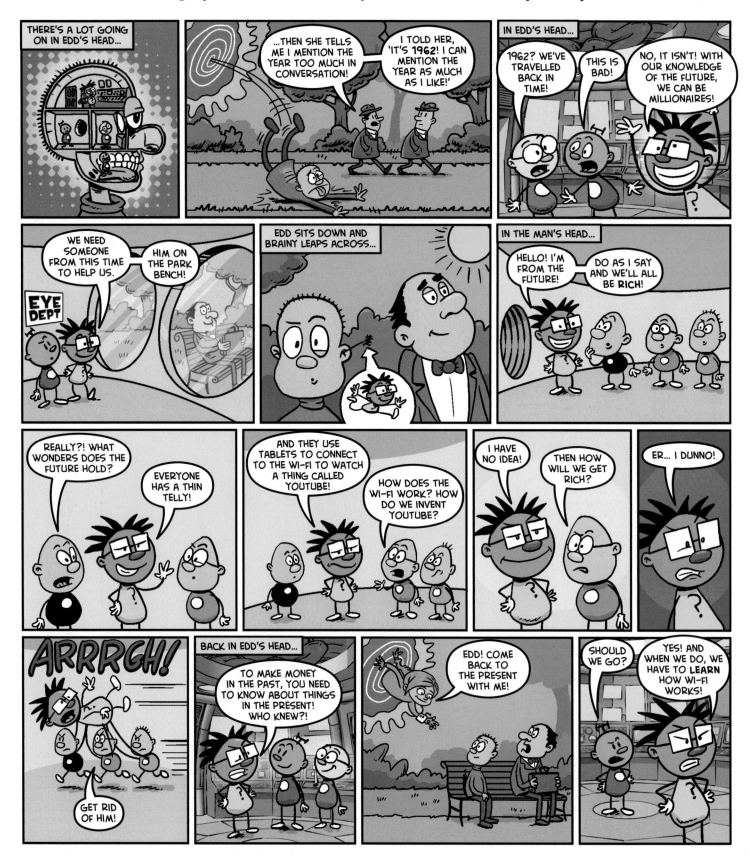

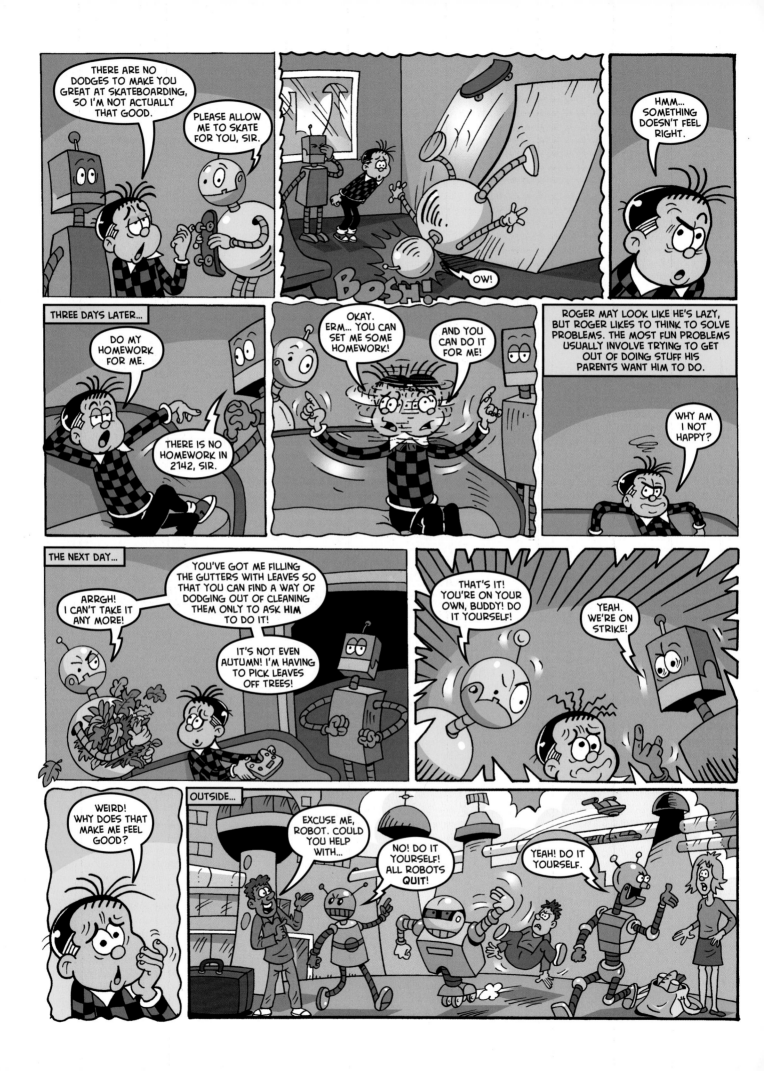

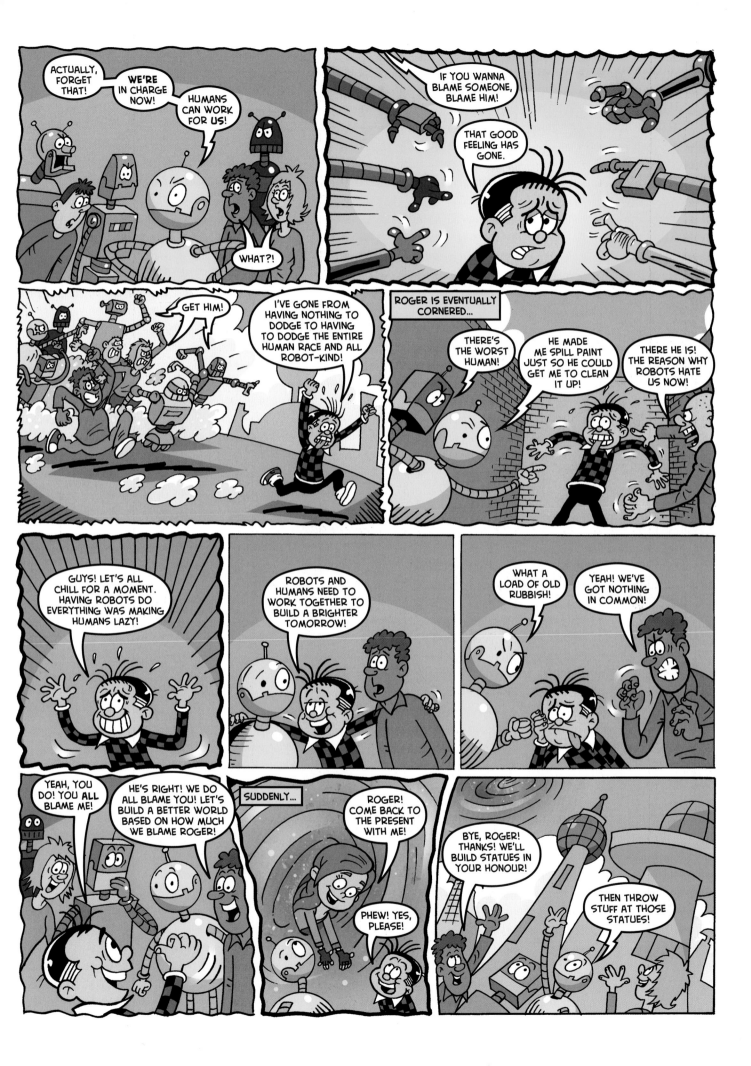

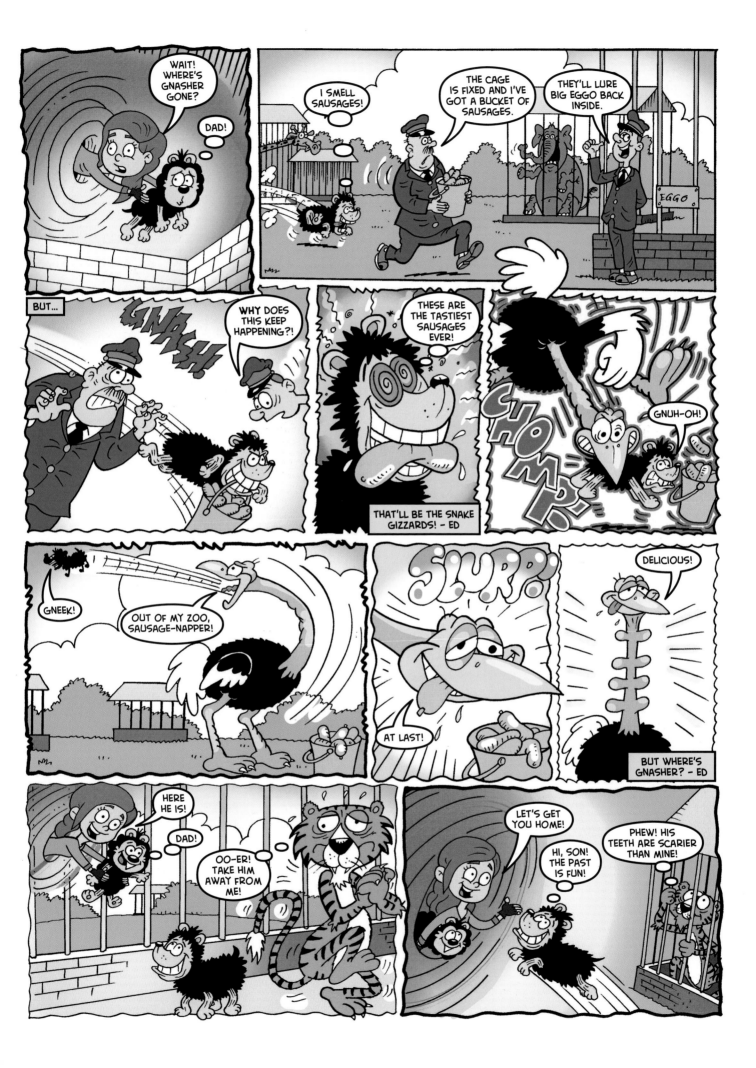

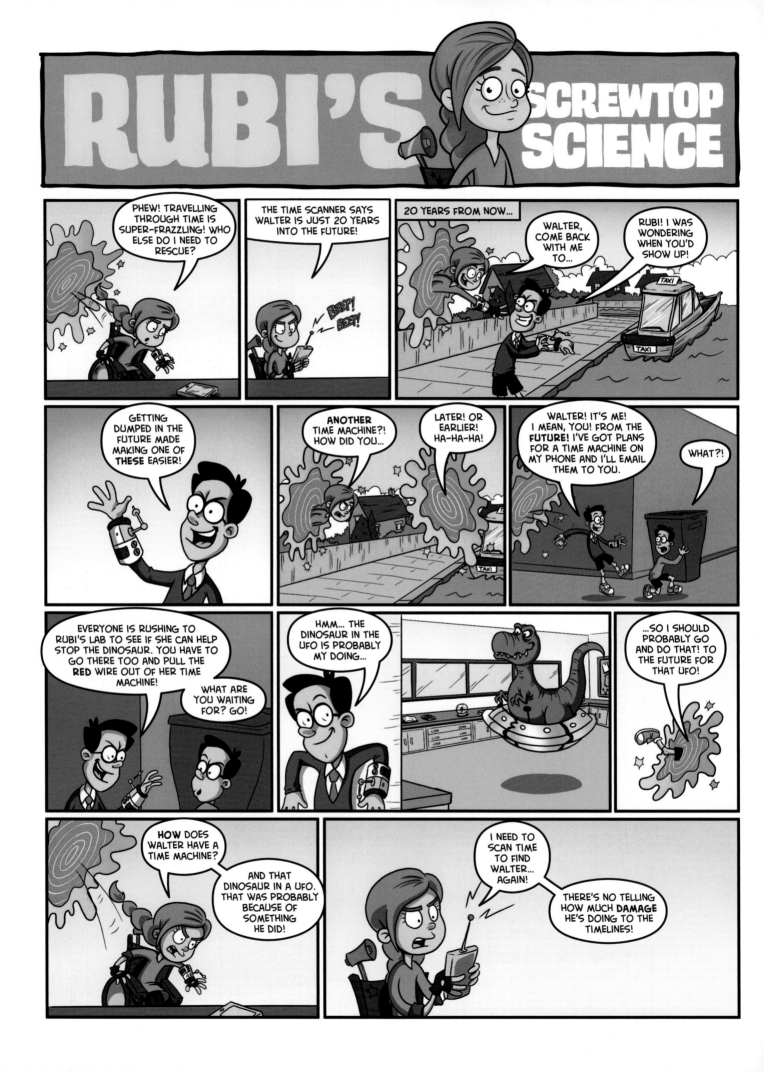

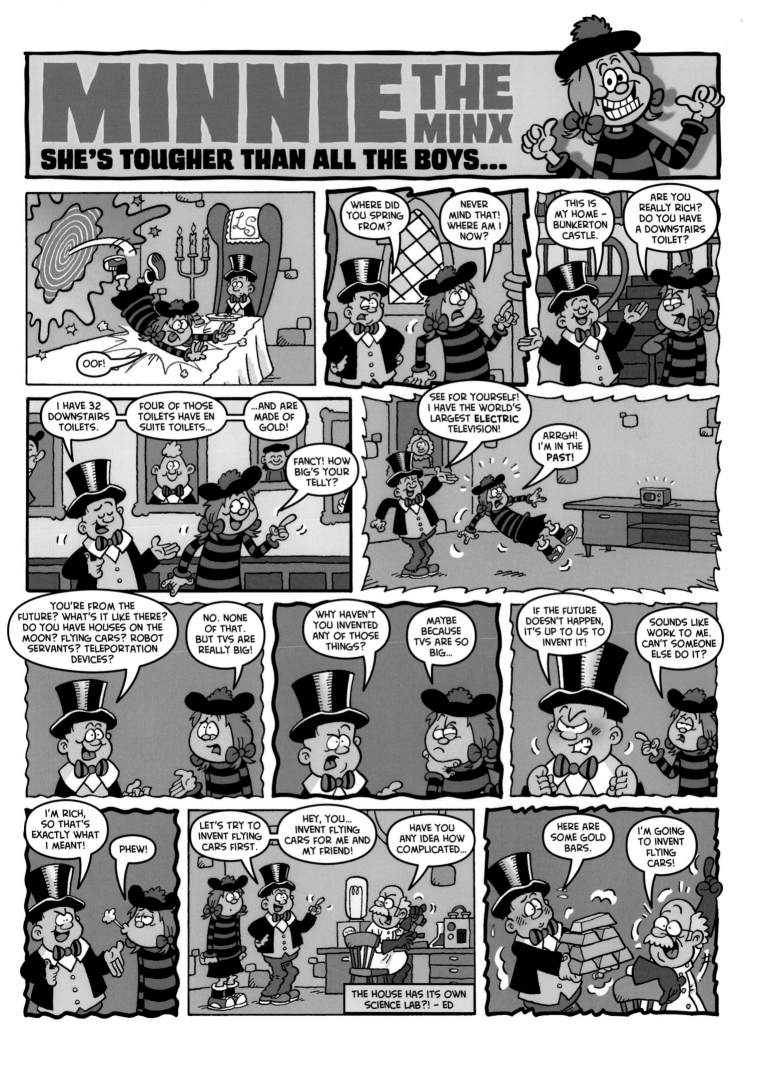

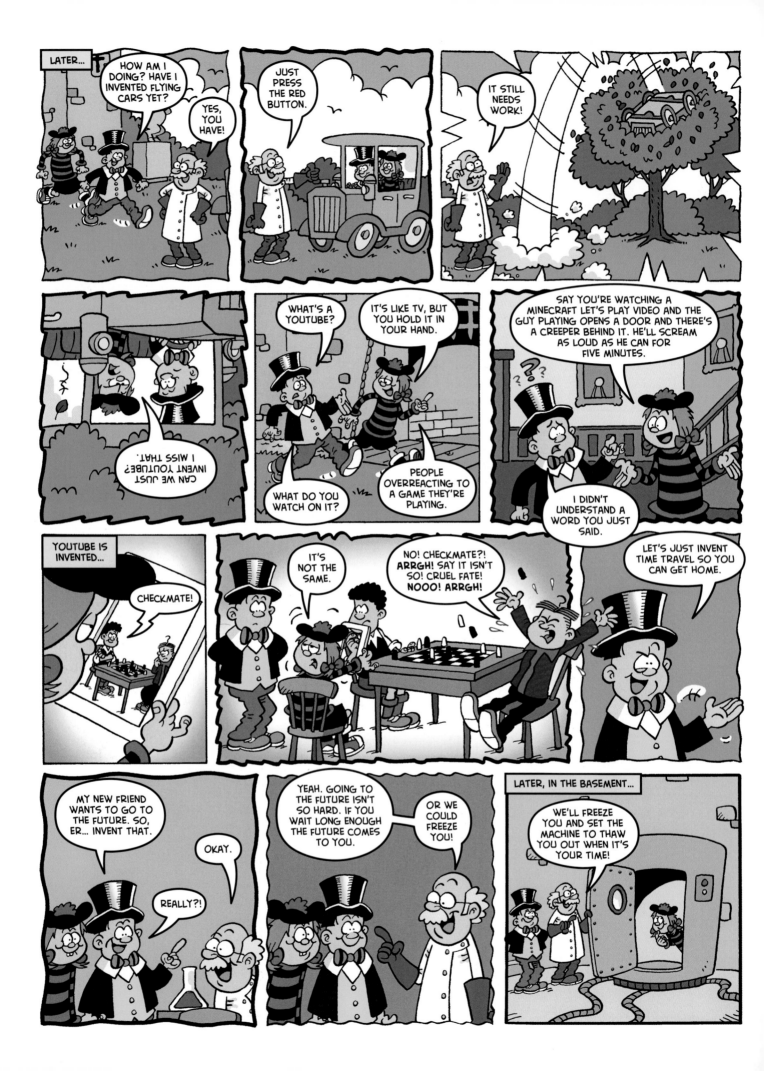

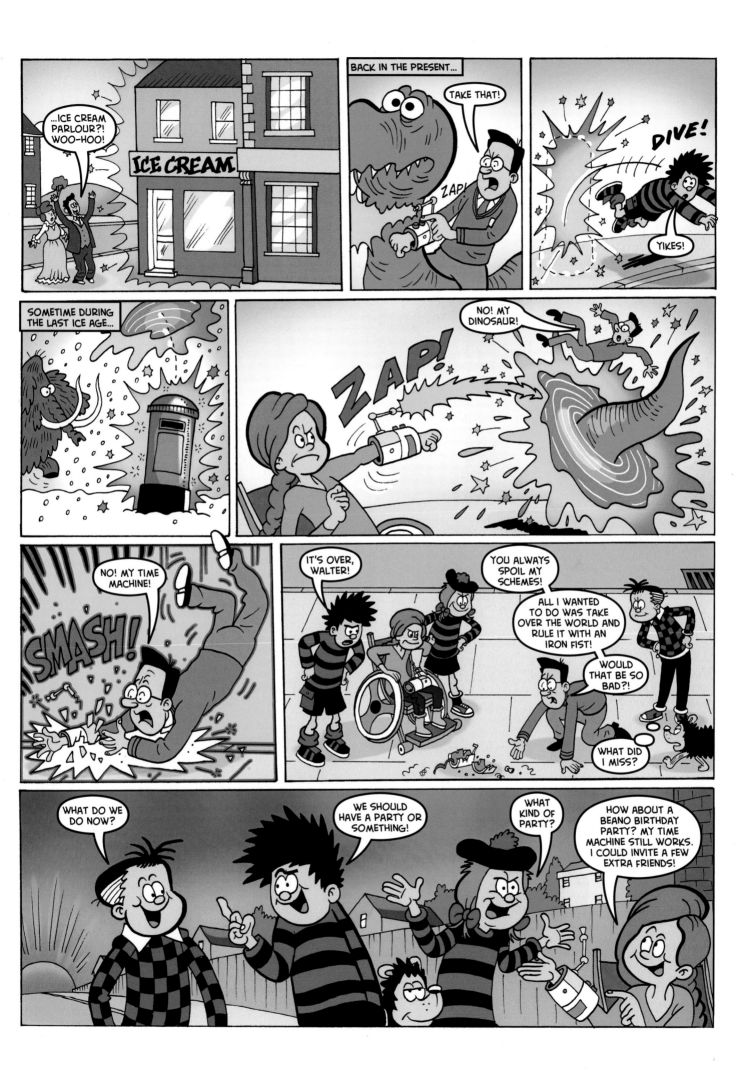

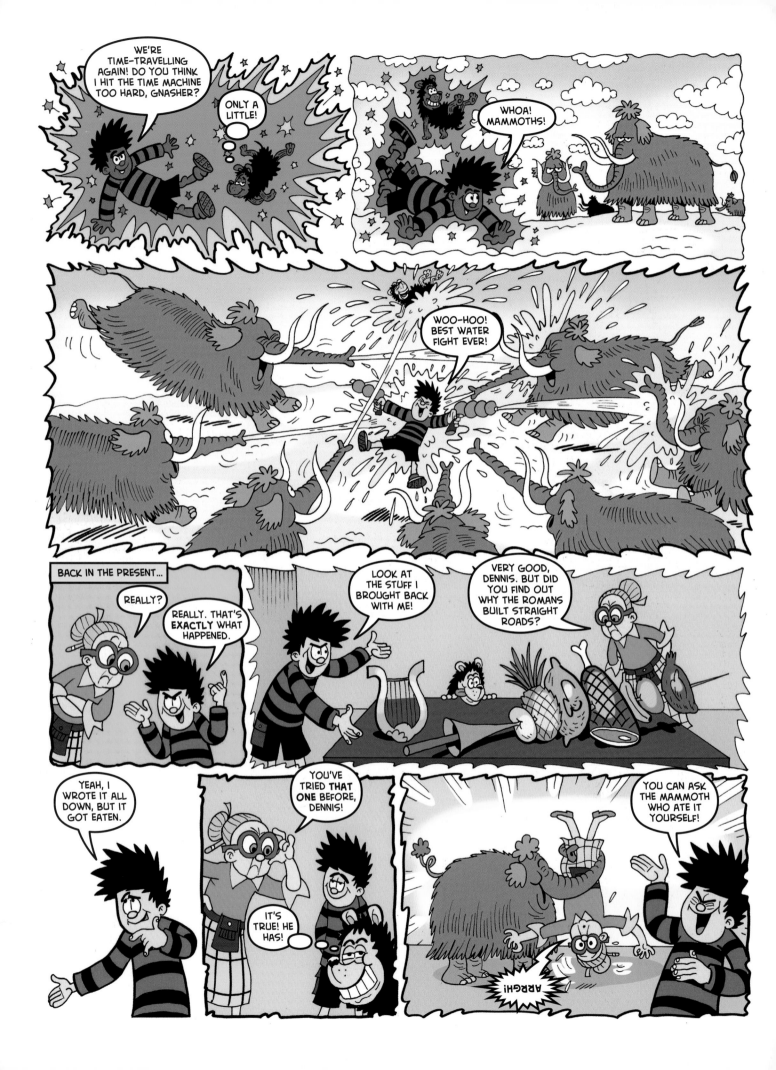

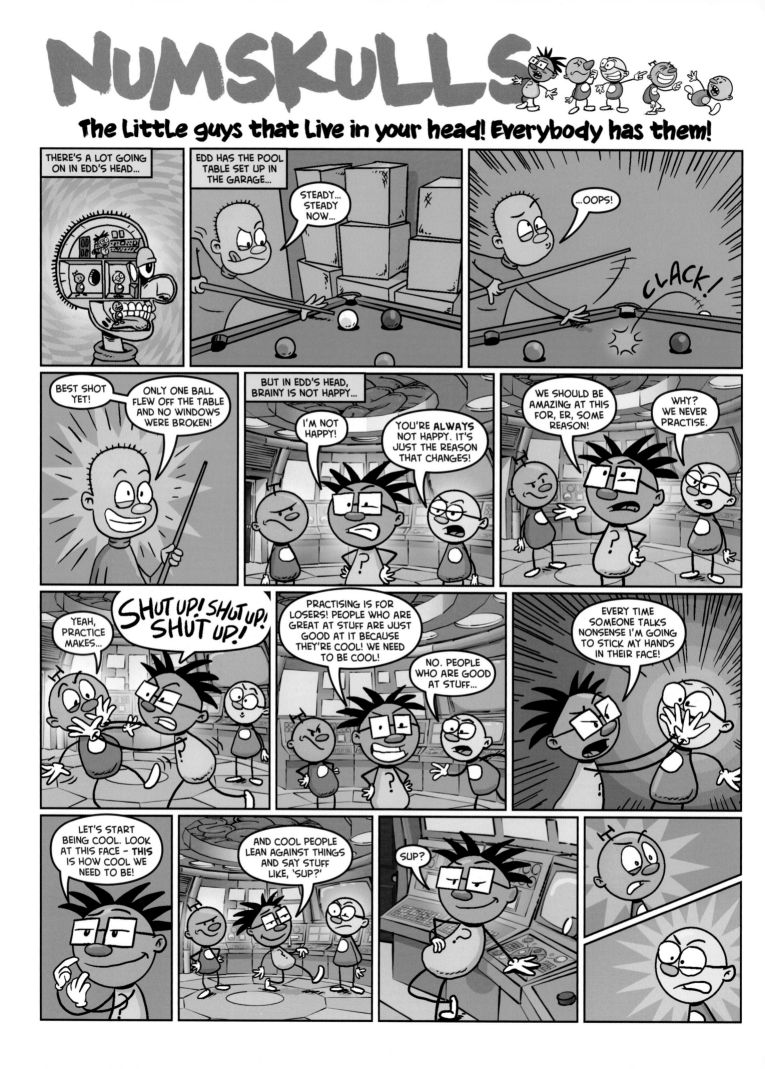

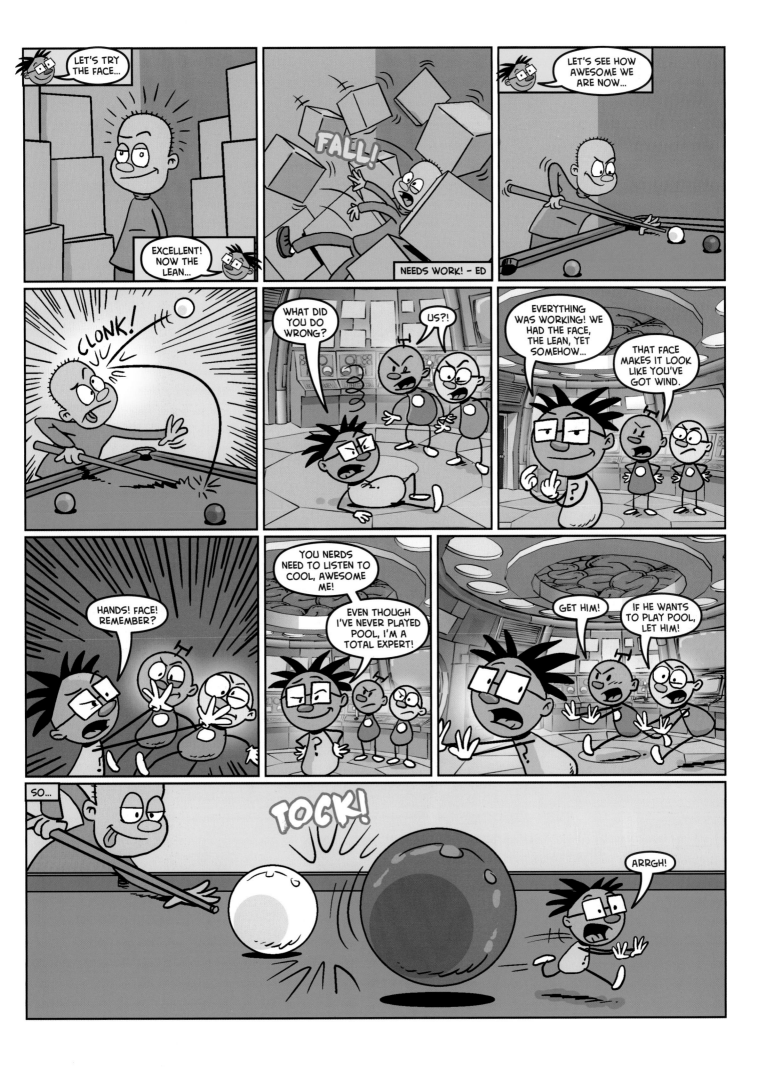

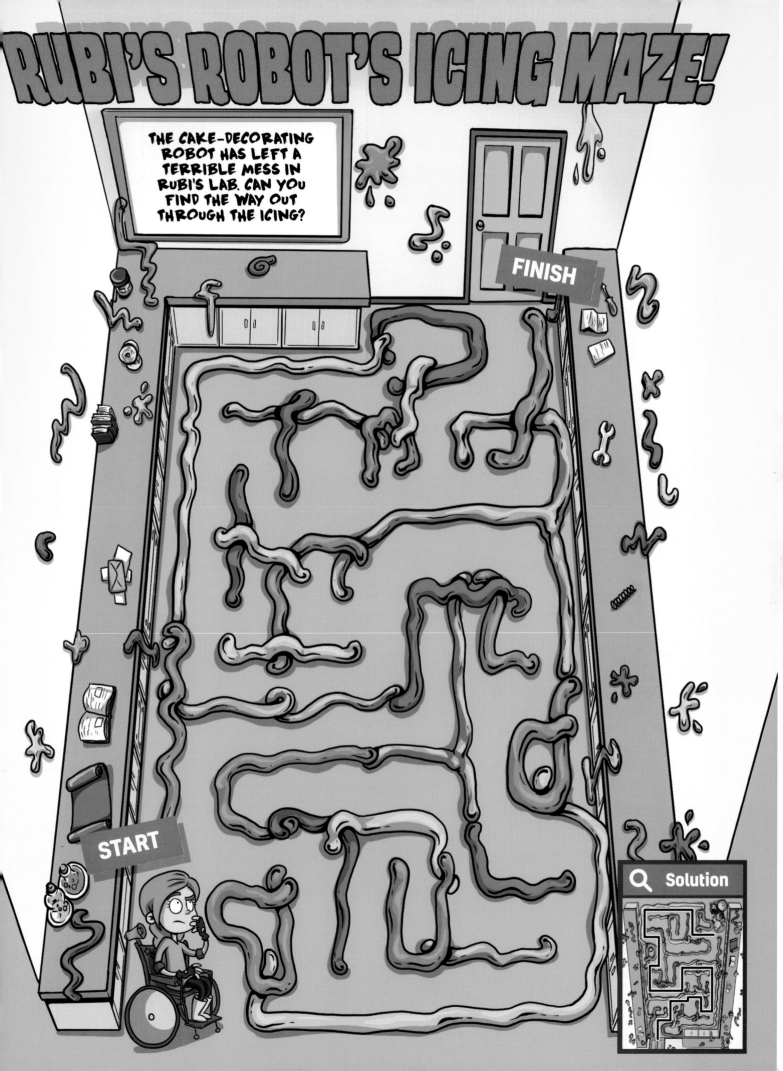

RUBI'S ROBOT'S ICING MAZE!

THE CAKE-DECORATING ROBOT HAS LEFT A TERRIBLE MESS IN RUBI'S LAB. CAN YOU FIND THE WAY OUT THROUGH THE ICING?

FINISH

START

Q Solution

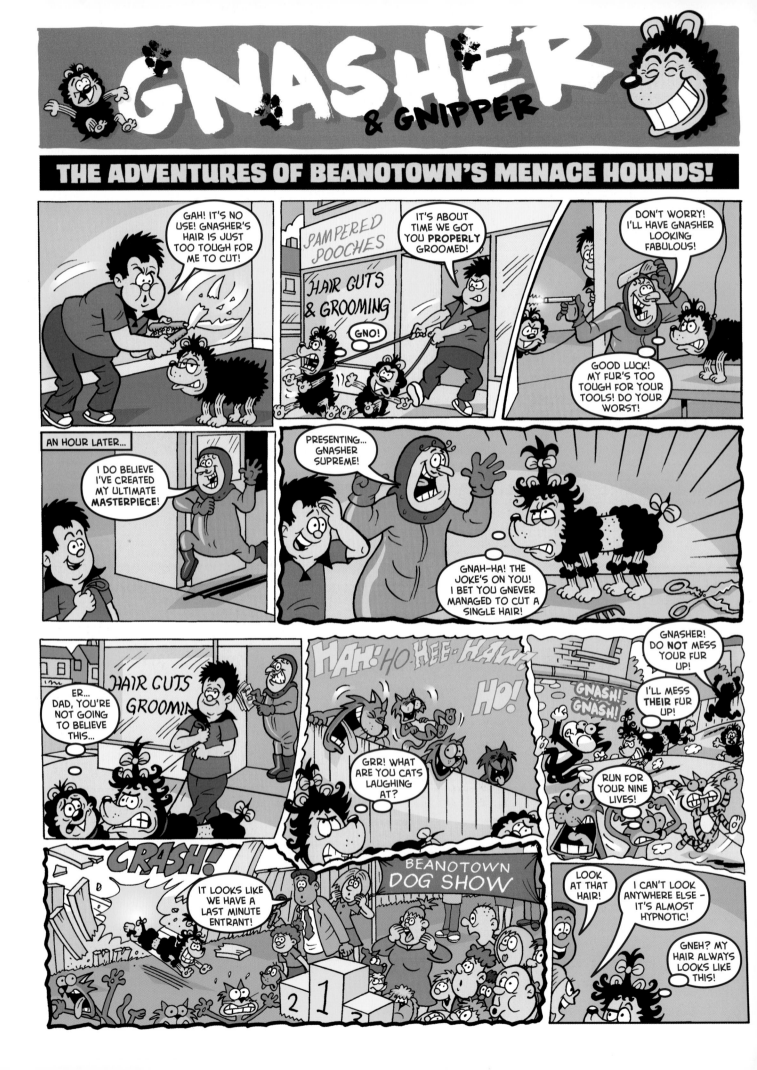

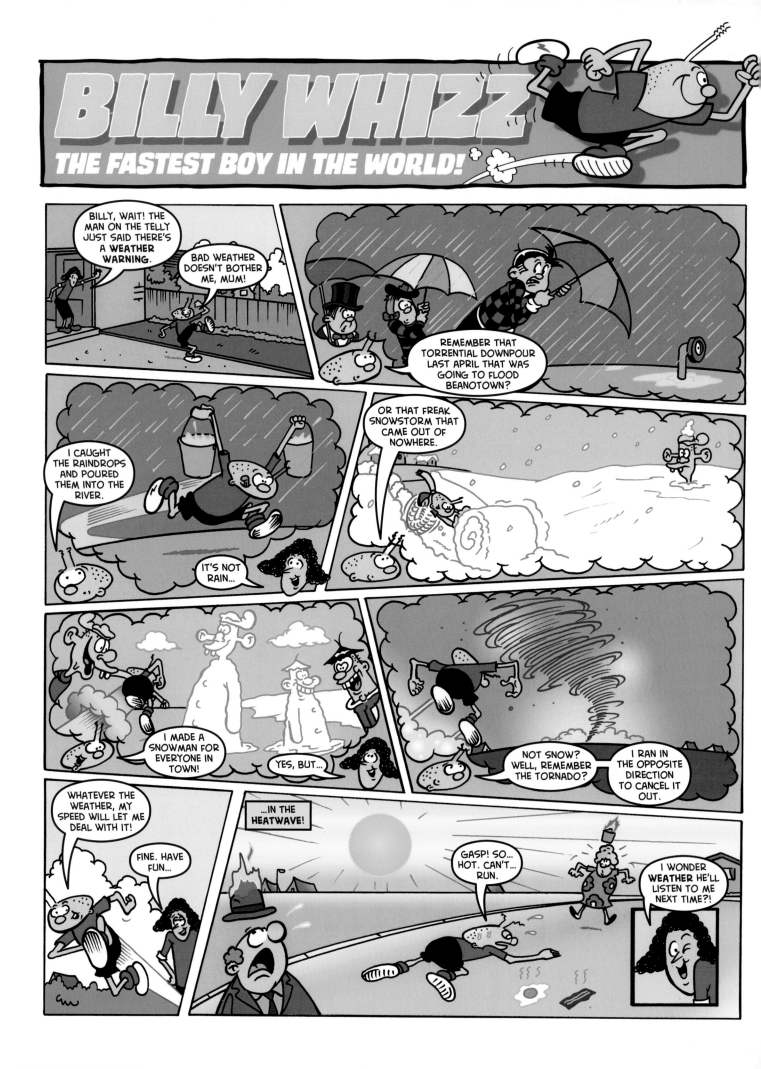

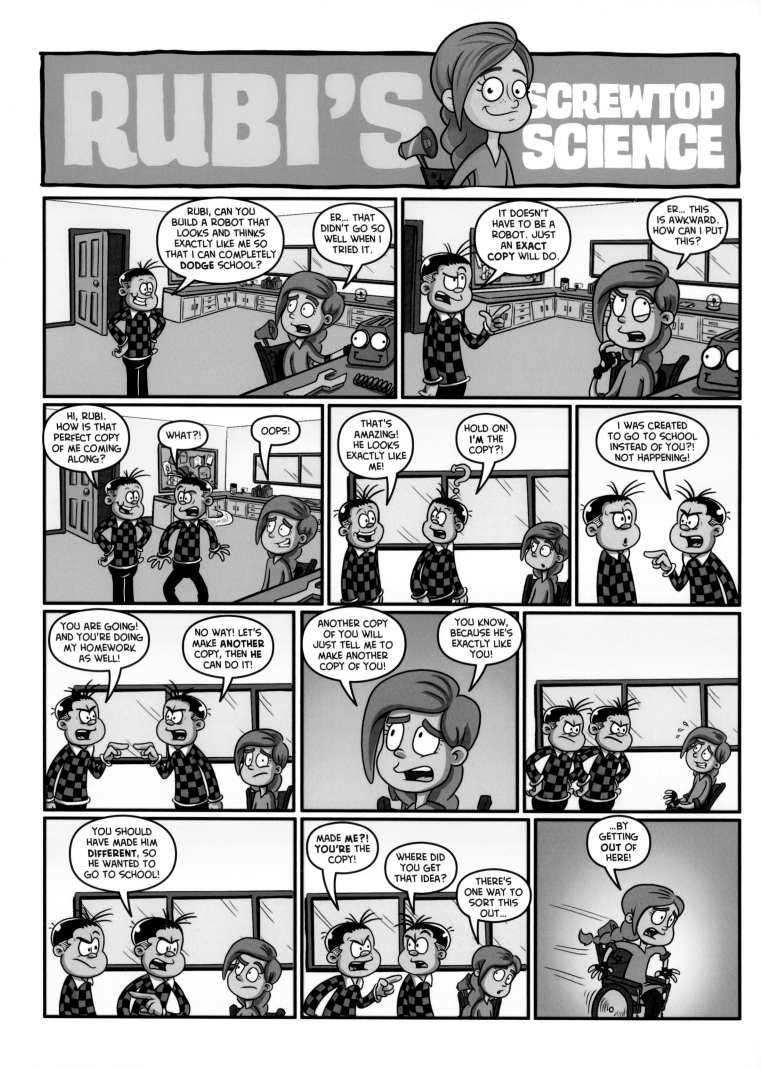

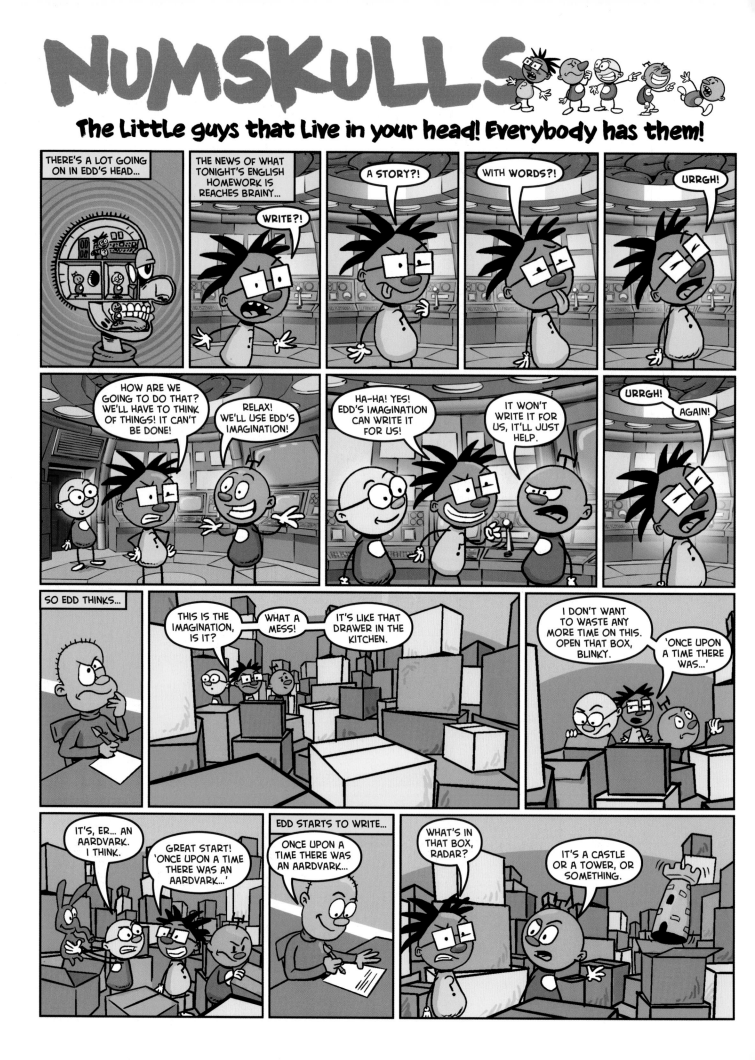

WHERE'S BRAINY?

Brainy is lost in Edd's imagination. Can you help the other Numskulls find him?

For bonus points, can you count how many unicycles there are?

Q Solution

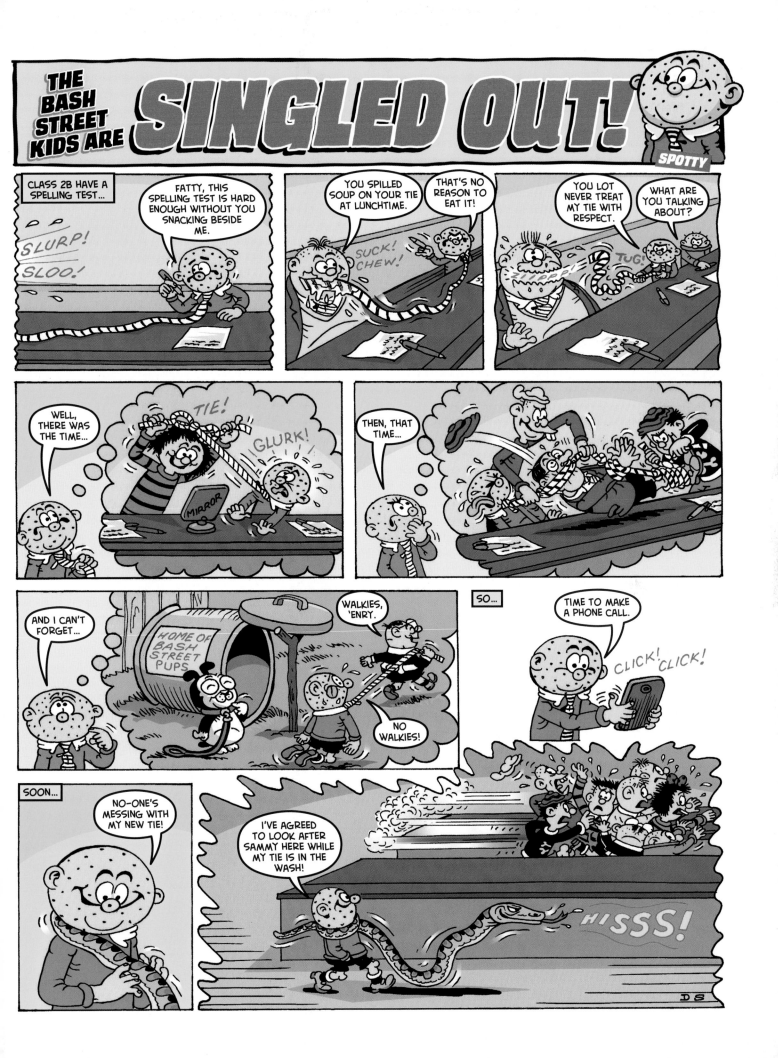

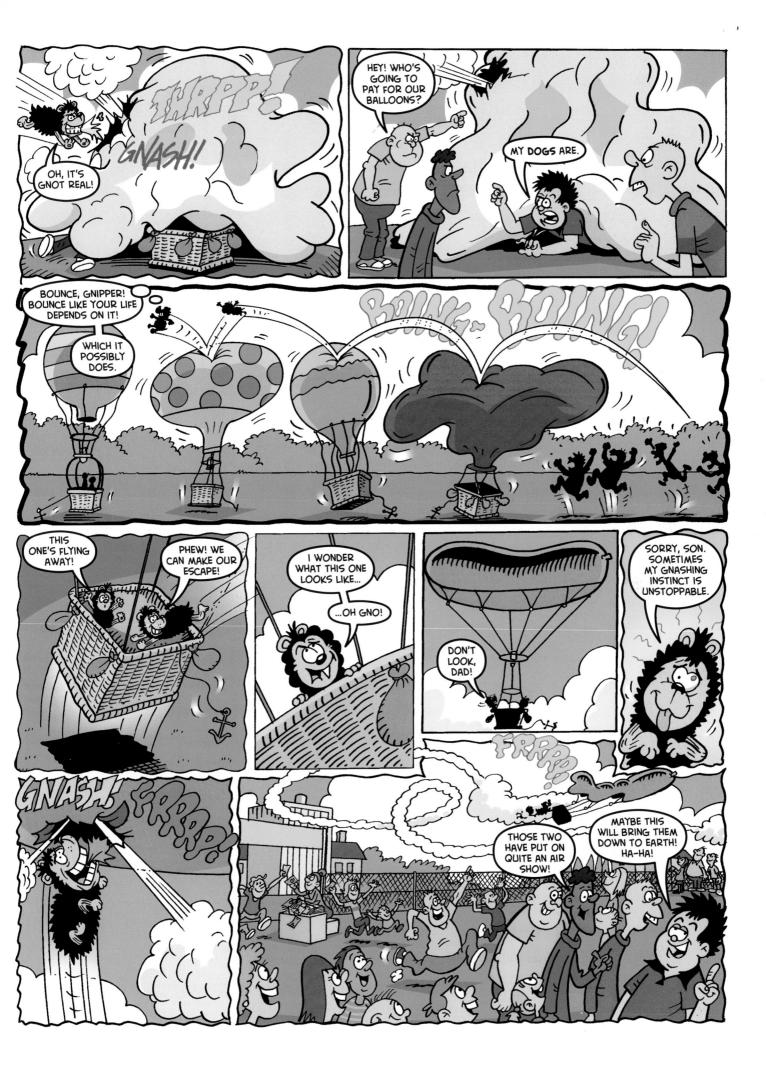

DODGES OF THE DEEP!

Roger has set up eight more dodges at the swimming pool. Can you find them all?

- The shark fin dodge ☐
- The octopus dodge ☐
- The submarine dodge ☐
- The "How Deep?" dodge ☐
- The upside-down dodge ☐
- The diver dodge ☐
- The fishing dodge ☐
- The polo dodge ☐

20,000 LEAGUES

WHIZ!

Solution

THINK YOU CAN HANDLE ALL THIS EVERY WEEK?

MEGA PUZZLES!

GENIUS JOKES!

EPIC COMICS!

AMAZING PRANKS!

PLUS LOADS MORE AWESOMENESS!

BEANO

ON SALE EVERY WEDNESDAY!